Editorial Project Manager
Dona Herweck Rice

Editor
Jennifer Overend Prior, M.Ed.

Editor-in-Chief
Sharon Coan, M.S. Ed.

Art Coordinator
Denice Adorno

Imaging
Alfred Lau

Product Manager
Phil Garcia

Publishers
Rachelle Cracchiolo, M.S. Ed.
Mary Dupuy Smith, M.S. Ed.

Grammar, Usage & Mechanics

Level 3

Author

Andrea Trischitta, M.A/M.A.T.

Teacher Created Materials, Inc.
6421 Industry Way
Westminster, CA 92683
www.teachercreated.com
ISBN-0-7439-3558-6
©2001 Teacher Created Materials, Inc.
Reprinted, 2003
Made in U.S.A.

Grammar, Usage, and Mechanics

A nonfiction reading & writing program • A nonfiction reading & writing program

Table of Contents

Nouns

What is a *noun*? A noun is a person, place, or thing.

Examples:

Person: stewardess, father, teacher, friend

Place: playground, office, mountain, family room

Thing: noodle, desk, telephone, pebble

There are other types of nouns, too.

Proper Noun

A *proper noun* is the name of a specific person, place, or thing.

Person: Michael Jordan, George Bush, Batman, Harry Potter

Place: Connecticut, Empire State Building, Mississippi River

Thing: Granny Smith Apple, Lucky Charms, Mountain Dew

Abstract Noun

An *abstract noun* names something that can be talked about, but cannot be seen or touched. Abstract nouns include courage, fear, Christianity, racism, and happiness.

Collective Noun

A *collective noun* names a collection of people, places, and things.

Collective nouns include class, team, and jury.

Grammar, Usage, and Mechanics

A nonfiction reading & writing program • A nonfiction reading & writing program

Solve the Riddle

For the following clues, guess the appropriate noun that fits each description.

1. I wear a spacesuit and rocket into the sky. Because there is no gravity, I am weightless. From my window in my ship, I see Earth.

   Who am I? _____

2. Be careful here or you could get burned—or frozen! It can be a dangerous place, because of the knives, but it's a yummy place, too. Greasy plates are cleaned in a soapy sink and scraps of food are thrown in the garbage.

   What place am I? _____

3. Although it has only two wheels, it goes really fast. For safety, it is best to wear a helmet. Usually, only one person sits on the seat, although another passenger can sit behind the driver. It is similar to a bicycle, only this form of transportation needs gasoline.

   What is this? _____

Did you guess these nouns correctly? The first noun was a person—an astronaut. The second noun was a place—a kitchen. The third noun was a thing—a motorcycle. Think of one other clue you could add to each riddle. Share your ideas.

Astronaut _____

Kitchen _____

Motorcycle _____

Your Turn

Think of a person, a place, and a thing that you can describe through clues. Write your clues on a piece of paper. Read these to the class or post them on a bulletin board. If you described the noun accurately, then all of the class answers should be the same.

Use the guide below to help make your clues.

Person _____

How I can describe this person?

Place _____

How can I describe this place?

Thing _____

How can I describe this thing?

Extension activity: Take a blank piece of paper and fold it in half to make a card. Write a riddle on the front of the card using your clues. On the inside, write the solution to your riddle. Include an illustration of the noun. Have a classmate solve your riddle.

Nouns, Nouns, Everywhere

Read the sentences below. Underline the nouns, including the proper nouns.

1. The dog is barking in the yard.

2. Shelly came over to my house.

3. I like to eat pizza with extra cheese and mushrooms.

4. At recess I play games with my friends.

5. I watched television after dinner.

6. My bird likes to get out of her cage.

7. The sun was shining on the lake.

8. I picked oranges and pears with David.

9. Have you seen the new slide at the park?

10. My mother gave me new pens, pencils, and erasers.

11. We went to visit my aunt in Texas.

12. I got new shoes and socks at the store.

In the space below, write a sentence using two nouns.

_____

_____

Grammar, Usage, and Mechanics

Your Whatsamajig Did What?

The following sentences contain silly (pretend) nouns. Rewrite each sentence, replacing the silly nouns with real nouns. Share your sentences with the class. Discuss how the sentences change depending upon the nouns chosen.

1. Geragogo fed his kadoozle some lingarangs.

   _____

2. The zanto roared into the miskit.

   _____

3. Under the tornee waited a sleeping alowawa.

   _____

4. Starving, Kaliyun begged for two hazumumps.

   _____

5. Bobozee threw his nemuf into the olontbah.

   _____

6. Emyrodz and his yackshamash walked to the takreree.

   _____

7. Isabydoi rode her bigabat to slandozma.

   _____

8. Randorall walked sadly after he fell into the lantonurnip.

   _____

9. A little feelo and wanawaldo played a sillibarom.

   _____

10. At the conordno, maleemamamu were sung.

    _____

Grammar, Usage, and Mechanics

A nonfiction reading & writing program • A nonfiction reading & writing program

A Room Full of Nouns

Look at the picture below. On page 9, write at least twenty nouns that you see in this room. Share your discoveries with your classmates.

A Room Full of Nouns (cont.)

The nouns I see in this bedroom are:

1. _____

2. _____

3. _____

4. _____

5. _____

6. _____

7. _____

8. _____

9. _____

10. _____

11. _____

12. _____

13. _____

14. _____

15. _____

16. _____

17. _____

18. _____

19. _____

20. _____

Your turn! On another paper, draw a picture of your dream bedroom. Label the picture with twenty nouns. Share pictures and nouns with the class. Try to include people, places, and things.

Grammar, Usage, and Mechanics

A nonfiction reading & writing program • A nonfiction reading & writing program

Person Brainstorm

In the space provided, write as many nouns as you can that are people, yet not specific people. Then, think of a proper noun (specific person) to fit the occupation listed. Samples are provided.

Person	Proper Person
1. actor	Jim Carrey
2. writer	E.B. White
3. athlete	Michael Jordan
4.	
5.	
6.	
7.	
8.	
9.	
10.	
11.	
12.	
13.	
14.	
15.	
16.	
17.	
18.	
19.	
20.	

Proper Nouns in Our Town

For the following list of nouns, write proper nouns of people, places, and things that are in your town, city, or surrounding area. For the "Things" column, you need to consider things found commonly in your area, such as popular brands and fads.

People

Noun	Proper Noun
1. mayor	_____
2. principal	_____
3. teacher	_____
4. superintendent	_____
5. librarian	_____
6. nurse	_____
7. dentist	_____
8. governor	_____

Things

Noun	Proper Noun
1. clothing	_____
2. food	_____
3. cereal	_____
4. drink	_____
5. car	_____
6. toy	_____
7. movie	_____
8. book	

Places

Noun	Proper Noun
1. school	_____
2. college	_____
3. museum	_____
4. library	_____
5. river	_____
6. restaurant	_____
7. historical landmark	_____
8. kids' hangout	_____

Grammar, Usage, and Mechanics

A nonfiction reading & writing program • A nonfiction reading & writing program

Abstract Noun Art Show

Abstract nouns are nouns that you can't see or touch. Abstract nouns include jealousy, freedom, hope, joy, innocence, love, greed, hate, air, dream, anger, prejudice, and racism.

These nouns are abstract because, although you know what they mean, there isn't anything you can see or touch. However, through art you can draw what these abstract nouns mean to you.

A. Respond to the questions in the space provided.

What is freedom? _____

Who represents freedom? _____

What represents freedom? _____

What places represent freedom? _____

B. Using magazine pictures and drawings, create a class bulletin board of images that symbolize "freedom."

C. Brainstorm a list of abstract nouns.

_____   _____   _____

_____   _____   _____

_____   _____   _____

Choose one abstract noun and make a collage that the noun symbolizes.

Abstract noun: _____

Who symbolizes this noun? _____

What things reflect this noun? _____

What places represent this noun? _____

Collective Nouns

Collective nouns represent groups of things. From the list of collective nouns, fill in the blank with the collective noun that best fits the sentence.

batch	school
fleet	pod
bunch	army
flock	bouquet
litter	pride

1. On the boat tour, we saw a _____ of whales!

2. Our picnic was ruined because an _____ of ants invaded our basket!

3. Mom and I baked a _____ of cookies for Back-to-School Night.

4. The sign said, "A _____ of puppies born. Free! Call 555-4678!"

5. At the fruit stand, you can buy a _____ of grapes.

6. At the aquarium, a _____ of fish swam toward the coral.

7. The _____ of lions slept in the warm sun.

8. A _____ of ships sailed in the harbor.

9. For my mother's birthday, my dad brought home a _____ of her favorite flowers.

10. At dusk, a _____ of geese flew over our house.

Think of other collective nouns and write them in sentences.

Grammar, Usage, and Mechanics

A nonfiction reading & writing program • A nonfiction reading & writing program

ABC Noun Book

For each letter of the alphabet, think of three nouns that begin with each letter. Create an alphabet book of these nouns with illustrations. Try to think of at least one noun from each category (person, place, or thing).

	Person	Place	Thing
A			
B			
C			
D			
E			
F			
G			
H			
I			
J			
K			
L			
M			
N			
O			
P			
Q			
R			
S			
T			
U			
V			
W			
X			
Y			
Z			

Grammar, Usage, and Mechanics

A nonfiction reading & writing program • A nonfiction reading & writing program

Find the Nouns

Underline the nouns in each sentence.

1. The barber shaved off the boy's hair.

2. A clump of hair lay on the floor.

3. The boy looked at his reflection in the mirror—he screamed in horror!

4. "My hair! My curls! What has the barber done?"

5. Smiling, the barber handed the boy a lollipop.

6. "A lollipop will not make my hair grow!" the boy cried.

7. The boy felt his bald head with his hand.

8. The boy jolted upright and realized he had been dreaming.

9. Relief and happiness flowed through the boy.

10. His fingers felt his brown hair, still on his head, and he drifted off into dreamland.

Extension activity: Add one adjective to each sentence.

Grammar, Usage, and Mechanics

A nonfiction reading & writing program • A nonfiction reading & writing program

Common to Proper

Underline the nouns in the sentences. Rewrite the sentences using proper nouns.

1. The policeman chased after a burglar running down the street.

   _____

2. When my brother wakes up, let's go to the store.

   _____

3. Can you buy me cereal, candy, and apples?

   _____

4. We went to the beach.

   _____

5. The president is visiting our town tomorrow.

   _____

6. My grandparents traveled overseas on a plane.

   _____

7. I picked flowers.

   _____

8. I am inviting the girls to my party at a restaurant.

   _____

9. This book is awesome.

   _____

10. Birds fly to other places in cold weather.

    _____

Capital ABC's

For each letter, write a proper noun for each category—person, place, thing. Remember to capitalize proper nouns.

	Person	Place	Thing
A			
B			
C			
D			
E			
F			
G			
H			
I			
J			
K			
L			
M			
N			
O			
P			
Q			
R			
S			
T			
U			
V			
W			
X			
Y			
Z			

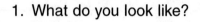
Describe Yourself!

What is an *adjective*? An adjective is a word that describes a noun. Adjectives help show the reader what people, places, or things look, sound, taste, smell, or feel like. Use plenty of adjectives to answer the following questions.

1. What do you look like?

2. Describe your personality.

3. Describe your talents.

Extension: Compile all of the information above and make a collage of adjectives describing you!

Opposites Attract

For each adjective, think of one or more antonyms.

Adjective	Antonym
1. old	1.
2. pretty	2.
3. wet	3.
4. dirty	4.
5. bright	5.
6. heavy	6.
7. cute	7.
8. long	8.
9. smart	9.
10. fast	10.
11. cold	11.
12. hungry	12.
13. hairy	13.
14. dishonest	14.
15. skinny	15.
16. kind	16.
17. fun	17.
18. asleep	18.
19. small	19.
20. juicy	20.

Think of more adjectives that have opposites.

Adjective	Antonym
_____	_____
_____	_____
_____	_____

Challenge: Choose ten adjective opposites and illustrate them in a book.

Find the Adjectives

Underline the adjectives in the following sentences.

1. The ugly witch stirred the gurgling potion in her iron cauldron.

2. Amid the red tulips, two gray squirrels chased each other's bushy tails.

3. A mountain goat nibbled sweet, green grass.

4. The elementary school students lined up for afternoon recess.

5. Awaiting the stern judge's sentence, the courtroom was quiet.

6. The scared mouse scurried into its little hole.

7. Splash your tired face with cold water to wake up.

8. We tossed a huge rock into the pond and heard a loud splash.

9. Becky licked her raspberry lollipop.

10. Craig wandered down the street searching for his lost watch.

Choose two sentences above and rewrite them using your own adjectives.

_____

_____

Read sentences 1–10 without the adjectives. In the space below, respond to the question, "What do adjectives do to sentences?" Share your opinion with the class.

_____

_____

_____

Grammar, Usage, and Mechanics

A nonfiction reading & writing program • A nonfiction reading & writing program

Add an Adjective

For each sentence, add an adjective that makes sense. Share your sentences with the class and discuss your choices. Then draw a picture of one of the sentences at the bottom of the page.

1. The baby is adorable, _____, and pudgy.

2. The witch's broom is fast, _____, and made of straw.

3. In the garden, I grew large, _____ tomatoes.

4. Chugging up the hill, the car made loud, _____ noises.

5. The bunny had a white, _____ tail.

6. All day we played in the cold, _____, and icy snow.

7. After a day at the beach, Susan was hot, _____, and sandy!

8. Tonya handed the brown, _____ football to Ryan.

9. The old, _____ man entered the hospital on crutches.

10. Her pretty, _____, and sparkling eyes lit up when she opened the present.

We Are All Unique

Write a list of adjectives about a good friend.

_____   _____

_____   _____

_____   _____

_____   _____

Write a list of adjectives about a good teacher.

_____   _____

_____   _____

_____   _____

_____   _____

Write a list of adjectives about a good child.

_____   _____

_____   _____

_____   _____

Write a list of adjectives about a good parent.

_____   _____

_____   _____

_____   _____

Choose one of the lists above and write a paragraph describing that person.

_____

_____

_____

_____

Grammar, Usage, and Mechanics

A nonfiction reading & writing program • *A nonfiction reading & writing program*

I'm Sick!

Okay, so you don't want to go to school because you do not feel well. Nevertheless, you need to convince your mom or dad that you are really, truly sick. Write one or more adjectives on each line and also use verbs to describe how you are feeling. Use these to write a one-paragraph letter to your mom or dad describing how you feel. You do not have to use all of the examples. (Feel free to change the sentences as needed.)

1. I have a _____ throat.

2. My throat is _____.

3. My _____ eyes hurt.

4. My eyes _____.

5. I have a(n) _____ stomach.

6. My stomach _____.

7. I have a _____ headache.

8. My head _____.

9. I have a _____ earache.

10. My ears _____.

Read your pretend letter to the class to determine who is the most sick. Draw a picture below of what you look like when you are sick. Be creative!

Clearer Sentences

The following sentences need adjectives. Read each sentence and determine what adjectives need to be added, changed, or taken away to improve it.

Example:

The man who has a lot of money goes to the store where food is sold and buys bakery items that are delicious and fresh.

Possible revision: The rich man goes to the grocery store and buys delicious and fresh baked goods.

How else could you revise the sentence?

_____

_____

_____

The dog, that was rolling in a puddle filled with dirt is about to have a bath in water that is the correct temperature and has soap bubbles.

Revision:

_____

_____

_____

The baby with no hair on her head and water flowing from her eyes had a diaper on that did not smell good.

Revision:

_____

_____

_____

Grammar, Usage, and Mechanics

A nonfiction reading & writing program • A nonfiction reading & writing program

Matching

What is an *adverb*? Adverbs describe verbs, adjectives, and other adverbs. Adverbs often end with the letters *ly*.

Choose the adverb from the box that best fits each sentence and describes the verb. Share your choices with the class. (Be sure to capitalize where necessary.)

ferociously	loudly
brightly	mysteriously
sadly	joyfully
beautifully	quietly
rapidly	quickly

1. Every type of flower grows _____ in Grandma's garden.

2. The carolers sang _____ on our front steps.

3. _____, the magician disappeared.

4. Jacqueline cried _____ because she couldn't find her mother in the crowded store.

5. Tiptoe _____ because your father is napping.

6. The balloon floated into the sky _____.

7. _____, the lion roared.

8. The river flowed _____ and the rafters were afraid.

9. The wicked witch cackled _____ and all the trick-or-treaters covered their ears.

10. Shining _____, the full moon guided the hikers through the woods.

Adding Description

Add adverbs to the following sentences. (Use words that end with *ly*.) Share your choices with your classmates. Discuss how certain adverbs have the ability to change the meaning of the sentence.

1. The boat bounced _____ over the water.

2. The cat crept _____ near the mouse.

3. The children laughed _____ at the magician's tricks.

4. The boy walked _____ down the crowded beach.

5. The rocket zoomed _____ into the sky.

6. The baby cried _____ from his crib.

7. The sky turned dark _____.

8. The ballet dancer moved _____ across the stage.

9. The puppy whimpered _____ at his empty bowl.

10. The soldiers marched _____ into battle.

Challenge: Underline one of the sentences from above. Before each noun, think of an adjective to add to the sentence. Draw a picture of the sentence you have chosen. Write the sentence below the illustration.

Adverb Magic

Rewrite each word to make it an adverb by adding *ly*. Then, write a sentence with the adverb. Read the sentences to the class.

1. clear _____

   sentence: _____

2. happy _____

   sentence: _____

3. nice _____

   sentence: _____

4. angry _____

   sentence: _____

5. hungry _____

   sentence: _____

6. quick _____

   sentence: _____

7. fierce _____

   sentence: _____

8. mischievous _____

   sentence: _____

9. nervous _____

   sentence: _____

10. awkward _____

   sentence: _____

Presto Chango!

Circle the adjective in each sentence. Then, change the adjective into an adverb. Finally, rewrite the sentence with the adverb.

Example: The ferocious lion roared at the zookeeper.

Adjective: ferocious

Adverb: ferociously

Revised sentence: The lion roared ferociously at the zookeeper.

1. The quick runner crossed the finish line.

   Adjective:

   Adverb:

   Revised sentence:

2. The happy boys swam in the creek.

   Adjective:

   Adverb:

   Revised sentence:

3. The nice waitress smiled at her customers.

   Adjective:

   Adverb:

   Revised sentence:

4. The angry man hollered at the taxi.

   Adjective:

   Adverb:

   Revised sentence:

5. The hungry children ate their lunches in the cafeteria.

   Adjective:

   Adverb:

   Revised sentence:

Grammar, Usage, and Mechanics

A nonfiction reading & writing program • A nonfiction reading & writing program

Name That Verb

What is a verb?

A verb is a word that expresses action or being. A verb tells what someone or something does or what someone or something has or is.

The trainer rides the elephant. (The verb *rides* expresses action.)

That elephant is enormous. (The verb *is* expresses what something is.)

For each sentence below, change the underlined word or words to a stronger verb. Rewrite each sentence.

1. The angry man was <u>talking</u>. _____

   _____

2. He <u>moved</u> like a rabbit._____

   _____

3. Rain was <u>dropping</u> from the sky. _____

   _____

4. She <u>told</u> a secret. _____

   _____

5. We <u>ate</u> the pizza quickly. _____

   _____

6. The old car <u>drove</u> up the hill. _____

   _____

7. The girl <u>jumped</u> off the diving board. _____

   _____

8. The angry cat <u>made a noise</u>. _____

   _____

9. The baby <u>moved</u> on the floor._____

   _____

10. The blender <u>stirred</u> the milkshake. _____

    _____

Grammar, Usage, and Mechanics

A nonfiction reading & writing program • A nonfiction reading & writing program

Look at What I Can Do!

Write a list of verbs that tell what you can *do*. Remember, these verbs will be action verbs! From your brainstormed list, choose three to act out for the class.

Can You or Can't You?

For each sentence, circle the verb and determine whether it is an action or non-action verb. Write the word action or non-action on the line.

Example: Lilly tapped her pencil on her desk.

The verb is tapped. Can a person tap? Yes. Therefore, it is an action verb.

1. I dashed across the finish line. _____

2. Dad took out the garbage. _____

3. Tyrone is young. _____

4. Nadine pedaled her bicycle. _____

5. Grandma slurped her soup. _____

6. Kristin's desk was messy. _____

7. The duck waddled into the pond. _____

8. Anna and Marie are sick. _____

9. I am really excited. _____

10. The eagle soared through the sky. _____

Grammar, Usage, and Mechanics

A nonfiction reading & writing program • A nonfiction reading & writing program

Helping Verbs

The following are helping verbs. Helping verbs "help" other verbs, usually action verbs. Study the list of helping verbs. Things to remember: 1) Helping verbs are always verbs. 2) The word "not" is not a verb. This includes *n't*. Use this guide to help you find the helping verbs.

is	am	might
was	were	are
has	have	had
do	does	did
be	been	shall
can	will	should
could	would	must
may		

For the following exercise, circle each verb. Don't forget the helping verbs! On each line, write both the helping verb and the action verb on the appropriate lines.

	Helping Verb(s)	Action Verb
1.		
2.		
3.		
4.		
5.		
6.		
7.		
8.		
9.		
10.		

1. Marcus should have been studying.

2. After dinner, you may eat dessert.

3. Mr. Winthrop might not know your instructor.

4. Shall the children enter the auditorium now?

5. Suzanna must have been sleeping during the fireworks.

6. Could someone please fix my bike tire?

7. The tickets are being placed in the bowl.

8. Carmen will mind if we do not ask him to the party.

9. Must you always argue with me?

10. I am learning my helping verbs.

Our Amazing Bodies

Our bodies are capable of doing many things. For the following pictures, write three action verbs that these "body parts" can do.

foot

nose

_____

_____

_____

_____

_____

_____

mouth

ear

_____

_____

_____

_____

_____

_____

hand

finger

_____

_____

_____

_____

_____

_____

Extension Activity: Make a sketch of the human body, labeling what the above body parts can do. Other body parts to consider include legs, arms, heart, lungs, stomach, intestines, muscles, knees, elbows, and brain.

Grammar, Usage, and Mechanics

A nonfiction reading & writing program • A nonfiction reading & writing program

Time to Do What?

For each hour of the day, write an action verb that you do. Do not repeat any verbs.

12. _____

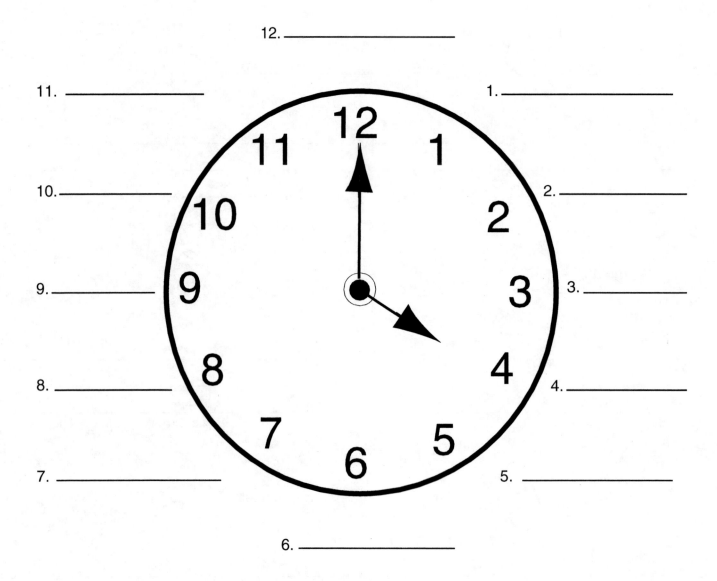

11. _____

10. _____

9. _____

8. _____

7. _____

6. _____

1. _____

2. _____

3. _____

4. _____

5. _____

Extension Activity: On another paper, write a sentence for each hour that contains the action verb you used. For example, *At seven o'clock I brush my teeth.*

Grammar, Usage, and Mechanics

A nonfiction reading & writing program • A nonfiction reading & writing program

Possessives

Possessives show belonging. The most common way to indicate possession is to add an apostrophe and an *s* to a noun.

> the boy's sailboat
>
> Mr. Smith's bag

When the noun is plural, indicating more than one, and it does not end in *s*, the proper way to indicate possession is to add an an apostrophe then an *s*.

> the children's playground
>
> the women's room

When the noun is plural and it ends in *s*, the proper way to indicate possession is to add an apostrophe only.

> the Jones' house
>
> the girls' room
>
> the teachers' lounge

Possessive pronouns are *my, his, her, your, our,* and *their*.

> my dog
>
> your house
>
> our family

I Think This Belongs to You

Rewrite each sentence, replacing the underlined words with a possessive. You may remove unneeded words from the sentence.

Example: The briefcase that belonged to the man was left at the subway station.

Revised sentence: The man's briefcase was left at the subway station.

1. The soccer balls that belonged to the team were tossed onto the field.

    Revised sentence:

2. Paintbrushes belonging to the artists were on the easels.

    Revised sentence:

3. The manes on the horses needed combing.

    Revised sentence:

4. The siren on the fire truck woke up the neighborhood.

    Revised sentence:

5. The angry face belonging to Mom told me I was in trouble.

    Revised sentence:

6. The brown bags that were held by the shoppers were filled with groceries.

    Revised sentence:

7. The nest that belonged to a bird held three eggs.

    Revised sentence:

8. The puppies that are owned by Billy are learning tricks.

    Revised sentence:

9. The net that the fisherman held contained fish.

    Revised sentence:

10. The engine in the car made horrible clunking sounds.

    Revised sentence:

Grammar, Usage, and Mechanics

A nonfiction reading & writing program • *A nonfiction reading & writing program*

A Picture Book of Plurals

If a word is singular, that means there is only one. If a word is plural, it means more than one. Plurals are made by *adding s, es, ies,* or changing the word *completely*. Rewrite the following words to make them plurals. Use a dictionary as a reference.

1. box _____

2. toy _____

3. child _____

4. man _____

5. lamp _____

6. puppy _____

7. goose _____

8. brush _____

9. potato _____

10. cucumber _____

11. clock _____

12. mouse _____

13. baby _____

14. wolf _____

15. crocodile _____

Make a picture book of singular and plural words of your choice. Choose ten words and write the singular and plural form. Then, design a picture book of the singular and plural words. You may illustrate or use computer graphics to complete your picture book. There should be a minimum of ten singular and plural pairs in your book. Your picture book should have a theme. For example, all of the words may be things that live in the ocean, things you might find in a fire station, etc.

Theme of picture book: _____

Singular	**Plural**
_____	_____
_____	_____
_____	_____
_____	_____
_____	_____
_____	_____
_____	_____
_____	_____
_____	_____

Grammar, Usage, and Mechanics

A nonfiction reading & writing program • A nonfiction reading & writing program

One or More Than One?

Rewrite each sentence using the appropriate singular or plural form of the nouns. The first one has been done for you.

1. Plumber fix pipe.

   Plumbers fix pipes. _____

2. Ape swing from vine.

   _____

3. Banana are delicious.

   _____

4. Seven boy and four girl are in my class.

   _____

5. The trains is coming down the track.

   _____

6. Pick one potatoes from our garden.

   _____

7. Teacher give us good book to read at homes.

   _____

8. My foot hurt from walking ten mile barefoot.

   _____

9. One mice just ran past me!

   _____

10. Will you set the table with these knife, fork, and spoon?

   _____

Grammar, Usage, and Mechanics

A nonfiction reading & writing program • A nonfiction reading & writing program

Misplaced Apostrophes

Rewrite the following sentences so that each apostrophe is in the correct place.

1. The balloons have'nt been tied to the chairs properly.

_____

2. The'yll be all right as soon as the doctor arrives.

_____

3. My aunt cou'ldnt believe I won the school spelling bee!

_____

4. Mr. Strung wouldv'e gone to the Olympics until he tore ligaments in his leg.

_____

5. Cant' you see im busy?

_____

6. I have no idea when il'l get a chance to clean my room.

_____

7. Coach Austin wont' see me unless I have a completed physical form.

_____

8. Iv'e heard shes' nice, but Im' not so sure.

_____

9. Wer'e going to the cookout on Friday, and we cant forget bug repellant!

_____

10. Ill tell you the secret about which yo'uve been bugging me.

_____

©*Teacher Created Materials, Inc.*   39   *TCM 3558 Grammar, Usage, and Mechanics—Level 3*

Grammar, Usage, and Mechanics

A nonfiction reading & writing program • A nonfiction reading & writing program

Contractor for Contractions

As a contractor, you need to determine the words that could be combined to form a contraction. Rewrite each sentence with a contraction.

1. Martha could have been a dancer, but she preferred gymnastics.

   _____

2. I do not think I will go to the nurse even though my throat hurts.

   _____

3. Rodriguez does not know the area well because he just moved here.

   _____

4. Our science teacher thinks we will do well on the state test.

   _____

5. He is not only my brother, but he is also my best friend.

   _____

6. Do not be afraid of the dark because I will leave a light on in the hallway.

   _____

7. The petshop owner told me the parrot would talk, but it will not even though I have done exactly what he said.

   _____

8. Let us go to the park tomorrow.

   _____

9. William cannot make me go on the roller coaster.

   _____

10. I cannot wait until tomorrow because we are going to the computer lab.

   _____

Grammar, Usage, and Mechanics

A nonfiction reading & writing program • A nonfiction reading & writing program

Capitalization

To capitalize means to write the first letter in uppercase. Here are some rules for capitalization.

Always capitalize:

- the word *I*
  I am going to the beach.

- the first word in a sentence
  When I leave, I expect you to follow!

- the names of people and places (proper nouns)
  Martha, Eric, and Shelby are working on a project about El Paso, Texas.

- words derived from proper nouns (proper adjectives)
  She speaks English, yet her German accent is noticeable.

- titles with people's names
  Senator Martin, Admiral Wittenburg, and Doctor Lopez were assigned to investigate.

- the title of a person (when used in place of that person's name)
  Hello, Doctor, I brought Mom with me to analyze the x-rays.

- days of the week and months
  On Friday, I am going to Minnesota for the month of August!

- the first letter of each word in a friendly letter greeting
  Dear Sarah Jane,

- the first letter of each word in a business letter greeting
  To Whom It May Concern:

- the main words in titles of books, movies, newspapers, television shows, plays, operas, musicals, or magazines
  In The Boston Globe *I read a review of* Chicken Fight, *a new movie based on the book* The Chicken Hutch Hides Secrets.

- school subjects if they are languages or actual class titles listed in a catalog
  I signed up for Spanish, World History, and Prehistoric Times.

- geographic locations when they name specific areas
  Miss Edna lived in the East until she married, then she moved to the South.

- holidays
  Thanksgiving is my favorite holiday because I visit with all of my cousins.

Never capitalize:

- persons' title when not used with a name or in place of a name.
  Call the doctor, I'm bleeding!

- the four seasons
  In the summer, I complain of the heat. In the winter, I complain of the cold!

- regular school subjects
  After language arts I have music, then health, and then it's time to go home!

- geographical directions
  Head north for three miles, then at the highway, head east.

Grammar, Usage, and Mechanics

A nonfiction reading & writing program • A nonfiction reading & writing program

All About Me

Use the capitalization rules (page 41) to complete the questionnaire.

Name: _____

Address: _____

Town/City: _____ State: _____

Parents' names: _____

Siblings: _____

Pets: _____

Mayor: _____

Governor: _____

State bird: _____ State flower: _____ State song: _____

Favorite book: _____

Favorite restaurant: _____

Favorite musician: _____

Favorite athlete: _____

Favorite animal: _____

Favorite month: _____

Favorite day of the week: _____

Favorite car: _____

Future occupation: _____

Best friend: _____

Grammar, Usage, and Mechanics

A nonfiction reading & writing program • A nonfiction reading & writing program

The I's Have It!

The word I is always capitalized. Rewrite each sentence correctly.

1. i would like to know if i'll be able to compete in the gymnastics competition.

   _____

2. Nancy thought i could wear my blue leotard.

   _____

3. If i do well on the balance beam, i could get a medal.

   _____

4. i wonder what music i should use for my floor routine?

   _____

5. i do love gymnastics!

   _____

Review

Use the capitalization rules to assist in rewriting the sentences.

1. uncle bill is a californian.

   _____

2. He is called dr. longley by his patients.

   _____

3. My uncle is a pediatrician.

   _____

4. When i see him, i always joke and say, "what's up, doc?"

   _____

5. Uncle bill is great to have around, because we always have a doctor in the house!

   _____

Days of the Week

Use the chart provided to keep a log of what you do during each waking hour for five days.

Day of Week

Time	Monday	Tuesday	Wednesday	Thursday	Friday
7 AM					
8 AM					
9 AM					
10 AM					
11 AM					
12 PM					
1 PM					
2 PM					
3 PM					
4 PM					
5 PM					
6 PM					
7 PM					
8 PM					

Choose the day you found most interesting and write a paragraph about that day. Be sure to use proper capitalization.

Friends and Family

Write the names of your immediate family members, relatives, and friends to total five people. Include the first name, middle name, nickname(s), and last name of each individual. (You should also include yourself in this assignment!) Follow appropriate capitalization rules.

1. First Name   Middle Name   Last Name   Nickname(s)   Relationship

2. First Name   Middle Name   Last Name   Nickname(s)   Relationship

3. First Name   Middle Name   Last Name   Nickname(s)   Relationship

4. First Name   Middle Name   Last Name   Nickname(s)   Relationship

5. First Name   Middle Name   Last Name   Nickname(s)   Relationship

Calendar of Events

List the twelve months, in order, in the boxes below. Using a calendar for assistance, write the holidays during each month. Include family birthdays and anniversaries. Be sure to capitalize the names of months, holidays, and people.

The holiday I look forward to most is: _____

Reasons why:_____

_____

Grammar, Usage, and Mechanics

A nonfiction reading & writing program • A nonfiction reading & writing program

Commas

Commas are used to indicate a pause between adjectives, clauses, phrases, or sentences.

Yoshika is a polite, friendly girl.

Although it is high tide, I think our canoe will fit under the bridge.

Mr. Evan is coming over, so clean the playroom!

A comma separates a city and state. If a sentence continues, also put a comma after the state.

One day I'd like to visit Boston, Massachusetts.

A comma separates two or more words in a list or series, including a comma before *and*.

I ate cotton candy, two hot dogs, and one funnel cake at the fair.

A comma is used after introductory words at the beginning of a sentence.

No, I can't come over after school.

Commas are used around interrupters.

My sisters, Whitney and Ellen, don't look alike.

A comma is used after the name of a person to whom someone is speaking.

Jerry, are you still sleeping?

A comma separates a quotation tag from a quotation.

The girl whined, "Why can't I have that doll?"

A comma is used after a greeting or closing in a letter to a friend or relative.

Dear Eddie,

Sincerely,

George

Grammar, Usage, and Mechanics

A nonfiction reading & writing program • A nonfiction reading & writing program

Where Do the Commas Go?

Add commas to the sentences below.

1. Mr. Ling my music teacher passed out our new song sheets.

2. You would like my dog Charlie.

3. Soda my favorite drink was served at the party!

4. Could I have the book *Freckle Face* on your desk?

5. Yes I would like some syrup for my pancakes please.

6. When she told the policeman Officer Pat she felt relieved.

7. I told Billy my next-door neighbor that I accidentally broke his window.

8. A cardinal my grandmother's favorite bird bathed in the bird bath.

9. No you can't play outside in the thunderstorm.

10. Mr. PJ's a comic strip character now has a computer game based on his adventures.

Coat of Arms

Complete the sentence starters below and then write your responses in the corresponding spaces on the coat of arms on page 50. Be sure to use commas in a series and a period at the end of sentences.

1. I like to eat _____

   _____

2. My favorite books or stories are _____

   _____

3. My favorite outdoor activities are _____

   _____

4. My favorite indoor activities are _____

   _____

5. These people are my role models: _____

   _____

6. My friends are _____

   _____

7. The places I like to go are _____

   _____

8. My favorite television programs are _____

   _____

9. When alone, I like to _____

   _____

Coat of Arms (cont.)

Punctuating Conversation

- Quotation marks go around the exact words a person speaks.

  "Marianne is sitting next to me," Sarah said.

- Periods, question marks, and commas go inside quotation marks.

  "Do you think you did well on the test? You didn't even study," Spencer said.

- Commas set off quotations.

  "Wow," breathed Marcus. "Did you see that sports car? One day I'm going to drive a car just like that."

- If the quote is one sentence, a comma is placed inside the first set of quotation marks, and another comma is used to set off the remainder of the sentence.

  "Tony," Jimmy demanded, "you didn't answer me. Are you playing whiffle ball or not?"

- When a quote is divided and it is two distinct sentences, begin the second sentence with a capital letter and no comma preceding the second sentence.

  "I was absent a few days last week," Sarah reminded Mr. Fredericks. "I didn't get a chance to study. So, shouldn't I take the test next week, when I'm ready?"

- When the speaker changes, begin the next quotation with a new paragraph.

  "The apples aren't ready for picking," said Farmer Bob. "Maybe you should come back next week."

  "Oh, you can count on that!" Nicky exclaimed.

What Did You Say?

The following sentences are missing quotation marks, commas, and end marks. Using the rules on page 51, punctuate the sentences.

1. Good luck in your game Mom called

2. Thanks I said and laced up my cleats

3. Don't forget your knapsack Mom warned

4. Why I asked

5. Well Mom replied I put juice and cookies in it

6. Mom I whispered as I hugged her you're the greatest

7. You, too, champ she said

8. I asked are you coming to my game

9. Mom laughed I wouldn't miss it for the world

10. Good I answered now I know I'll play better

Write a conversation you had with one of your friends or family members. Use correct punctuation.

Sentences

A sentence is a complete thought that begins with a capital letter, contains a subject and a verb, and ends with a period, question mark, or an exclamation point.

Subject

The subject of a sentence is whom or what the sentence is about.

Predicate (verb)

The predicate tells what the subject is doing.

> **Example:**
>
> A little boy fell into a mud puddle.
>
> Subject: a little boy
>
> Predicate: fell into a mud puddle

Run-on Sentence

A run-on sentence has too much information in one sentence without punctuation or transitional words.

> **Example:**
>
> After lunch, the children went into the backyard to play some played in the sandbox others climbed up the rope ladder and one drifted lazily on the swing.

Fragment

A sentence fragment is a sentence that is missing either the subject, the predicate, or does not complete a thought.

> **Example:**
>
> When the birds fly.
>
> The baby girl.

There are four types of sentences:

- **A *declarative sentence* ends with a period.**

  I threw a penny into the fountain.

- **An *imperative sentence* is a command or an order and ends with a period or exclamation point.**

  Give me a penny to throw into the fountain!

- **An *exclamatory sentence* ends with an exclamation point.**

  I made a wish when I threw my penny into the fountain!

- **An *interrogative sentence* is a question and ends with a question mark.**

  Do you think my wish will come true?

Grammar, Usage, and Mechanics

A nonfiction reading & writing program • A nonfiction reading & writing program

Determining Subject and Predicate

Write the complete subject and the complete predicate for each sentence in the spaces provided.

Example:

A. The telephone was ringing.

B. I answered the telephone.

	Subject	Predicate
A.	The telephone	was ringing
B.	I	answered the telephone

	Subject	Predicate
1. I draw with a crayon.	1.	
2. The crayon lay on the table.	2.	
3. We sailed past the lighthouse.	3.	
4. The lighthouse is one mile from shore.	4.	
5. The train is coming shortly.	5.	
6. I ride the train to work.	6.	
7. I collected shells at the beach.	7.	
8. Shells hid beneath the sand.	8.	
9 A napkin is on my lap for emergencies.	9.	
10. My face should be wiped with a napkin.	10.	

Stop That Run-On!

Rewrite each sentence to stop that run-on. (You will need to write more than one sentence for each run-on.) Add or take away words as needed.

1. After the fire we left our house and went to my aunt's house she let us stay there until the firemen told us it was safe to return home

   _____

   _____

2. When you do homework first you should find a nice quiet place to study make sure you have everything you need like pencils and paper you should turn off the television too.

   _____

   _____

3. Babysitting is hard work especially after a long day at school when I have gym class and scooter races I get tired and now there are two kids who want to go to the playground!

   _____

   _____

4. I love reading it is so great you get caught up in the book sometimes you actually think you are in the book!

   _____

   _____

5. When I go to sleepovers I bring my sleeping bag I also bring my favorite stuffed animal but I hide it at the bottom of my sleeping bag if other kids take out their stuffed animals then I take mine out but if they don't I keep it hidden so others don't think I'm a baby.

   _____

   _____

Fragments

Read the sentence fragments below. Rewrite each sentence so that it is complete. Share your revisions with the class.

1. and the boy decided

   _____

2. the computer suddenly

   _____

3. while studying in the school library

   _____

4. if you tell her

   _____

5. when Mr. Jones told me

   _____

6. after hearing the news

   _____

7. without crying the girl

   _____

8. could you please get

   _____

9. the cat on the step

   _____

10. under the sea, the fish

    _____

State, Demand, Question, Exclaim

For each group of sentences, write the type of sentence on the space provided: **declarative, interrogative, imperative,** and **exclamatory.**

1. The boy lost his toothbrush. _____

2. Where is your toothbrush? _____

3. I got a glow-in-the-dark toothbrush! _____

4. Give me my toothbrush. _____

5. The cave is haunted! _____

6. Don't go in the cave! _____

7. Where was the cave? _____

8. I explored a cave today. _____

9. Should Joshua go to the doctor? _____

10. Get on the scale so the doctor can weigh you. _____

11. Doctor Fred is the greatest! _____

12. Joshua got his yearly physical at the doctor's office. _____

Choose a noun from each list. Write a sentence on another paper using all three nouns. Then write more sentences in the same way.

People	Places	Things
teacher	bedroom	lemon
mail carrier	school	frog
police officer	playground	bicycle
grandmother	museum	mushroom
musician	skyscraper	rubber band
train conductor	beach	candle
waiter	mountain	hat

Grammar, Usage, and Mechanics

A nonfiction reading & writing program • A nonfiction reading & writing program

Write Your Own

Select a person, a place, and a thing. For each subject, write four different kinds of sentences.

Person _____

declarative _____

imperative _____

interrogative _____

exclamatory _____

Place _____

declarative _____

imperative _____

interrogative _____

exclamatory _____

Thing _____

declarative _____

imperative _____

interrogative _____

exclamatory _____

On separate papers, illustrate each group of sentences.

Combining Sentences

Two or more sentences can often be combined into one sentence. Commas and conjunctions (*and, or, but*) provide the transitions needed to make the sentence smooth.

Combining sentences makes stronger sentence structure. Here is an example:

Sentences: I like ice cream.
                 I like cookies.

Combined: I like ice cream and cookies.

Sentences:

1. Joshua ate a hamburger.
   Joshua ate French fries.

2. Terrence hit the drum.
   Terrence hit the cymbals.

3. Grandpa read a book.
   Grandpa read the newspaper.

4. Chickens clucked in the farmyard.
   Roosters clucked in the farmyard.

5. Boys played on the playground.
   Girls played on the playground.

6. Mom bought peas at the grocery store.
   Mom bought bread at the grocery store.
   Mom bought milk at the grocery store.

7. A bluebird ate at the birdfeeder.
   A cardinal ate at the birdfeeder.
   A chickadee ate at the birdfeeder.

8. The campers roasted marshmallows over the campfire.
   The campers roasted hot dogs over the campfire.

Combined:

1. _____
   _____

2. _____
   _____

3. _____
   _____

4. _____
   _____

5. _____
   _____

6. _____
   _____

7. _____
   _____

8. _____
   _____

Expanding Sentences

When you expand a sentence, you are avoiding short, choppy sentences and adding detail to make the sentence more interesting. Consider the following sentence.

Example: The car drove past.

What kind of car is it? Where is it driving? How is it driving?

Revision 1: The blue race car zoomed past the black and white checkered flags.

Revision 2: The old, rusty car sputtered past the horse farm.

For each sentence, do at least two of the following:

- replace the verb with a stronger verb
- add an adjective before each noun
- change one noun to a proper noun
- add adverbs to describe verbs

1. The boy in the uniform hit the ball over the fence.

2. A turtle walked down the bank to the stream.

3. The children at the park were on the swings.

4. A plane went up into the sky.

5. At the farm, the pigs wanted food.

6. Please put a blanket on the baby.

7. A balloon went up into the clouds.

8. A wolf makes noises at the moon.

9. The music playing on the radio is nice.

10. The girl wrote a letter to a friend.

Grammar, Usage, and Mechanics

A nonfiction reading & writing program • *A nonfiction reading & writing program*

Are You Talking to Me?

For each sentence, circle the correct word and write the word on the corresponding line.

1. Sam and _____ rode our bikes to town.
   (I, me)

2. _____ had on my new, red bike helmet.
   (I, me)

3. A crossing guard gave Sam and _____ the "Okay" to cross.
   (I, me)

4. We parked our bikes and Sam gave _____ the bike lock.
   (I, me)

5. "Dustin, can _____ trust you with the lock combination?" Sam asked.
   (I, me)

6. _____ nodded yes.
   (I, me)

7. We went to the ice cream shop and Sam and _____ got ice cream cones.
   (I, me)

8. The lady gave Sam and _____ rainbow sprinkles.
   (I, me)

9. _____ asked, "Sammy, may _____ taste your flavor?"
   (I, me)   (I, me)

10. "No way!" replied Sam, "_____ don't want to get cooties!"
    (I, me)

11. _____ laughed.
    (I, me)

12. Sam always liked to tease _____.
    (I, me)

Grammar, Usage, and Mechanics

Question of the Day

It's and *its* are often confused.

    It's means "it is."

    Its shows possession.

For each sentence, write the correct form of *its* or *it's* on the line. Use capitals when needed.

1. _____ a beautiful day to go bike-riding.

2. The banner read, "_____ a boy!"

3. The dog wagged _____ tail when the front door opened.

4. Do you know when _____ time for art class?

5. The tiger showed _____ fangs.

6. _____ eyes glowed mysteriously at midnight.

7. The sailboat made _____ way across the harbor.

8. A blanket of leaves covered _____ body.

9. The girl exclaimed, "_____ over there. Can you see _____ feathers?"

10. The flower wilted from _____ lack of water.

Types of Paragraphs

What Is a Paragraph?

A paragraph is a group of sentences centered around one idea or theme. When you write a story or report, you separate each idea into paragraphs. This makes it easier for the reader to understand.

Here is the basic structure of a paragraph:

A paragraph has a *topic sentence* that tells what the remainder of the paragraph will be about. Subsequent paragraphs relate to the first paragraph's main idea.

The next series of sentences are *supporting sentences*. Depending upon the type of paragraph, these sentences explain, describe, or narrate in order of important details.

The *concluding sentence* sums up the paragraph. It is important in the concluding sentence that you end the paragraph, and do not introduce new topics.

Types of Paragraphs

Narrative: Narrative paragraphs tell a story in chronological order.

Descriptive: Descriptive paragraphs describe something in great detail.

How-to: How-to paragraphs describe how to do something step-by-step.

Opinion: Opinion paragraphs explain a viewpoint.

What Do They Have in Common?

For each set of words, circle the word that does not belong. Decide what each set of words has in common.

1. shovel   pail   rake   umbrella   trowel

   What do the words have in common?

   _____

   _____

2. barrettes   gel   lipstick   ribbons   hairspray

   What do the words have in common?

   _____

   _____

3. shoes   pillow   nightlight   teddy bear   bed

   What do the words have in common?

   _____

   _____

4. apple   stapler   tape   crayons   erasers

   What do the words have in common?

   _____

   _____

Write your own list of common words, but put in a word that doesn't belong. Try to trick the reader! Share your list with the class and see if someone can guess the word that doesn't belong.

Grammar, Usage, and Mechanics

Supporting Role

Support your topic sentence. For each of the topic sentences listed below, write three original sentences that would make a well-structured paragraph. Be sure to include supporting sentences and a concluding sentence.

1. Reading books is one of my favorite things to do.

   _____

   _____

   _____

2. Setting the table for dinner is confusing.

   _____

   _____

   _____

3. Teachers should never give homework over the weekend.

   _____

   _____

   _____

4. Exercising is necessary to staying healthy.

   _____

   _____

   _____

5. The party I went to was a blast!

   _____

   _____

   _____

What Doesn't Belong?

Read the following paragraphs and cross out the sentences that do not belong. Then answer the question.

I love to go crabbing with my dad. We go to the docks where our crab trap is kept. It hangs on a rope into the water. It is high tide. We hoist the metal cage out of the water. Dad lets me put the bait in the middle of the trap. Today we are using a fish. The fish will attract crabs into the cage, because crabs eat fish. Fish eat smaller fish. We slowly lower the crab trap back into the water. Patiently, we wait. After a while, we lift the crab trap out of the water. There are three Blue Claw Crabs in the cage! They don't know how to get out of the trap. Carefully, my dad opens the latch, and shakes the crabs into a bucket filled with water. I wonder if my mom misses me? Then, the cage goes into the water again. The only thing better than crabbing with my dad is eating the crabs for dinner!

Is this paragraph *descriptive, how-to, opinion,* or *narrative*?

_____

Parents should let their kids walk to school by themselves, as long as their children follow some rules. Riding the school bus is fun. First, children should always take the same route to get to school. They should prove that they know how to get to and from school by letting their parents walk with them. I have a map of the United States. Second, children should always walk in the crosswalk, look both ways before crossing, and obey the crossing guard. Cars go when there is a green light. The most important rule is never talking to strangers, never getting in someone else's car, and knowing when to scream or run for help. So, if you want to walk to school, show your parents that you are able to follow the rules.

Is this paragraph *descriptive, how-to, opinion,* or *narrative*?

_____

The Missing Sentences

The following paragraph is missing a concluding sentence. Read the paragraph and write a sentence that sums up the paragraph.

I love going to the bakery. Every weekend my father takes me to buy breakfast treats. We walk the busy city streets and my stomach rumbles. We can always smell the bakery before we see it. The bakery is crowded, but the shelves are filled with fresh bread, glazed donuts, and apple turnovers. Inside the cases are chocolate eclairs, blueberry muffins, and sugar cookies. There is always a plate for sampling the new cakes and treats. While waiting our turn, I sample a raspberry tart. It is yummy. When it's our turn, I tell the lady that I'd like a sugar-covered jelly donut. It is delicious.

Concluding sentence: _____

The following paragraph is missing a topic sentence. Read the supporting and concluding sentences and write a strong topic sentence.

Topic sentence: _____

First, we got two bowls from the kitchen. Dana and I put on long-sleeve shirts and pants, because even though it was hot outside, we didn't want to get cut from the stickers and thorns. We walked down the path to the blackberry patch. Amid all the vines were huge blackberries the size of my thumb! We gently grasped the blackberries between our fingers and they fell right into the bowl. All afternoon Dana and I picked blackberries. We actually ate more than we picked! Our bowls overflowed with blackberries and we walked up the path to Dana's house. We shared the berries with everyone.

Choose two topic sentences from the list. Write a complete paragraph for each topic sentence on a lined sheet of paper.

1. The worst chore is cleaning my bedroom.

2. Having a pet will help one to learn how to take care of people.

3. Often I love being alone.

4. Learning to ride without training wheels is difficult.

5. Family vacations are special.

Grammar, Usage, and Mechanics

A nonfiction reading & writing program • A nonfiction reading & writing program

Proofreading Marks

Editor's Mark	Meaning	Example
≡	capitalize	they fished in lake tahoe.
/	make it lowercase	Five Students missed the Bus.
sp.	spelling mistake	The day was clowdy and cold.
⊙	add a period	Tomorrow is a holiday
ᵧ	delete (remove)	One person knew the the answer.
∧	add a word	Six were in the litter.
∧̣	add a comma	He planted peas corn, and squash.
∽	reverse words or letters	An otter swam in the bed kelp.
⌄	add an apostrophe	The childs bike was red.
⌄⌄	add quotation marks	Why can't I go? she cried.
#	make a space	He ate two redapples.
◡	close the space	Her favorite game is soft ball.
⌗	begin a new paragraph	to know. Next on the list . . .

Mistakes Happen

The following sentences contain misspelled words. Use the correct proofreading mark and then write the sentence correctly on the line below it.

1. Mabye we shud buy our aples over their.

   _____

2. Eye don't no why she ohways talks with her mouse full.

   _____

3. Tommorrow were going to where our butiful dresses to skool.

   _____

4. To ephelants wandered buy us, and we through peenuts to them.

   _____

5. In soccor, you knead to kick the ball with yure feet and knot yuse your hands.

   _____

Read the paragraph below. Use editing marks to correct mistakes in spelling and punctuation.

There is a large oak Tree in my backyard. I have always wanted to make a big pile of leaves to jump in. My dad spends so much time raking, he he always says, "No leaf pile. I've done enough raking this year." Then my dad got a leef blower. We were excited to see if it worked. My mom handed us rakes and we hoped we wouldn't be left raking the millions of oak. My dad filled the engine of the leaf blower with gas gasoline and pulled the handle. The leaf blower made a loud noise, but it did a great job We had so much fun roling in the and throwing them into the air. My mom said To my day, "Honey, do you think we should get a snow blower, too?

More Editing Practice

Proofread the sentences below, using editing marks. Add an adjective to each sentence. Then rewrite each sentence on the line.

1. For Halloween, I love to wearcostumes.

   _____

2. Isnt it a lovely Day.

   _____

3. I love to eat icecream.

   _____

Reverse words or letters and find the spelling mistakes. Use correct proofreading marks.

4. Long-fin tuna swam in the Ocean Atlantic in Ogust.

   _____

5. A hug bird flew over my house.

   _____

6. Did you hear the siren loud?

   _____

Add quotation marks and fix capitalization using appropriate proofreading marks.

7. hey mr. spenser i called can you help mom and my fix my Bike?

   _____

8. this is my favorite song, Said Lisa.

   _____

Add commas and apostrophes where needed using appropriate proofreading marks.

9. Arent we supposed to buy ice cream hot fudge whipped cream and cherries for the party were having tonight?

   _____

10. Well call you before the show. Youll be home, wont you?

   _____

Editor's Checklist

Use this list when editing your work.

❏ Don't worry about editing on your first draft. Let your creativity flow.

❏ Read your work aloud so you can tell if it is smooth and clear.

❏ Ask a friend or relative to read your work. Often, another person can find what needs to be changed.

❏ Put your work aside for awhile and then come back to it. With fresh eyes, you are likely to catch things you may have missed before.

❏ Check your mechanics:
  • Do all your sentences begin with a capital letter?
  • Do all your sentences end with the correct punctuation?
  • Have you been careful not to overuse exclamation marks?
  • Do all your proper nouns begin with capital letters?

❏ Have you checked to be sure all words are spelled correctly? (Don't rely on a spell checker!)
  • Are there any missing words?
  • Are there any extra words?
  • Have you used commas correctly?
  • Have you used apostrophes where they are needed?
  • Have you used quotation marks where needed?
  • Are your words spaced correctly?
  • Is your work easy to read and legible?

❏ Check your content:
  • Have you been clear about the topic of your writing?
  • Is it easy to tell what your story is about?
  • Have you used any special words or phrases that add to your story?
  • Have you used words that describe well?
  • Are there any words or phrases that are confusing?
  • Do you say the same thing more than once?
  • Are there any words or phrases that do not belong?
  • Are there any sentences that are awkward or that do not flow well?
  • Do you stay focused on your topic, or do you go in too many directions?
  • Is your writing interesting to your readers?
  • Have you considered what you could do to make your writing better?

Grammar, Usage, and Mechanics

A nonfiction reading & writing program • A nonfiction reading & writing program

Answer Key

Page 6

1. dog, yard
2. Shelly, house
3. pizza, cheese, mushrooms
4. recess, games, friends
5. television, dinner
6. bird, cage
7. sun, lake
8. oranges, pears, David
9. slide, park
10. mother, pens, pencils, erasers
11. aunt, Texas
12. shoes, socks, store

Page 7

Sentences will vary.

Page 13

1. pod
2. army
3. batch
4. litter
5. bunch
6. school
7. pride
8. fleet
9. bouquet
10. flock

Page 15

1. barber, boy's, hair
2. clump, hair, floor
3. boy, reflection, mirror, horror
4. hair, curls, barber
5. barber, boy, lollipop
6. lollipop, hair, boy
7. boy, head, hand
8. boy
9. relief, happiness, boy
10. fingers, hair, head, dreamland

Page 16

1. The <u>policeman</u> chased after a <u>burglar</u> running down the <u>street</u>.
2. When my <u>brother</u> wakes up, let's go to the <u>store</u>.
3. Can you buy me <u>cereal</u>, <u>candy</u>, and <u>apples</u>?
4. We went to the <u>beach</u>.
5. The <u>president</u> is visiting our <u>town</u> tomorrow.
6. My <u>grandparents</u> traveled overseas on a <u>plane</u>.
7. I picked <u>flowers</u>.
8. I am inviting the <u>girls</u> to my <u>party</u> at a <u>restaurant</u>.
9. This <u>book</u> is awesome.
10. <u>Birds</u> fly to other <u>places</u> in cold <u>weather</u>.

Grammar, Usage, and Mechanics

A nonfiction reading & writing program • A nonfiction reading & writing program

Answer Key (cont.)

Page 19

Answers may vary.

1. young
2. ugly
3. dry
4. clean
5. dark
6. light
7. ugly
8. short
9. dumb or stupid
10. slow
11. hot
12. full
13. bald
14. honest
15. fat
16. mean
17. boring
18. awake
19. large
20. dry

Page 20

1. ugly, gurgling, iron
2. red, two, gray, bushy
3. mountain, sweet, green
4. elementary school, afternoon
5. stern, quiet
6. scared, little
7. tired, cold
8. huge, loud
9. raspberry
10. lost

Page 21

Adjectives will vary. Examples given.

1. The baby is adorable, **sweet**, and pudgy.
2. The witch's broom is fast, **light**, and made of straw.
3. In the garden, I grew large, **red** tomatoes.
4. Chugging up the hill, the car made loud, **rattling** noises.
5. The bunny had a white, **puffy** tail.
6. All day we played in the cold, **white**, and icy snow.
7. After a day at the beach, Susan was hot, **tan**, and sandy!
8. Tonya handed the brown, **leather** football to Ryan.
9. The old, **feeble** man entered the hospital on crutches.
10. Her pretty, **blue**, and sparkling eyes lit up when she opened the present.

Grammar, Usage, and Mechanics

A nonfiction reading & writing program • *A nonfiction reading & writing program*

Answer Key (cont.)

Page 23
Sentences will vary.

Page 25
Answers will vary. Here are some suggestions.

1. beautifully
2. joyfully
3. mysteriously
4. sadly
5. quietly
6. quickly
7. ferociously
8. rapidly
9. loudly
10. brightly

Page 26
Answers will vary.

Page 27
Sentences will vary.

1. clearly
2. happily
3. nicely
4. angrily
5. hungrily
6. quickly
7. fiercely
8. mischievously
9. nervously
10. awkwardly

Page 28
Sentences will vary.

Page 29
Answers may vary.

1. yelling, screaming, shouting
2. hopped, jumped, leaped
3. sprinkling, pouring
4. whispered, tattled
5. gobbled, chomped, swallowed
6. chugged, sputtered, backfired
7. belly-flopped, dived, cannonballed
8. hissed, screeched
9. crawled, wobbled, rolled, fell
10. mixed, blended

Page 31

1. dashed/action
2. took/action
3. is/non-action
4. pedaled/action
5. slurped/action
6. was/non-action
7. waddled/action
8. are/non-action
9. am/non-action
10. soared/action

Grammar, Usage, and Mechanics

A nonfiction reading & writing program • A nonfiction reading & writing program

Answer Key (cont.)

Page 32

1. should have been/studying
2. may/eat
3. might/know
4. shall/enter
5. must have been/sleeping
6. could/fix
7. are being/placed
8. will/mind, do/ask
9. must/argue
10. am/learning

Page 33

Answers will vary.

foot: stomp, walk, crush

nose: smell, breathe, sneeze, sniff

mouth: chew, grind, eat, taste

finger: tap, touch, snap

hand: touch, feel, hold

eye: squint, observe, watch

Page 34

Each verb and sentence will vary.

Page 36

1. The soccer team's balls were tossed onto the field.
2. The artists' paintbrushes were on the easels.
3. The horses' manes needed combing.
4. The fire truck's siren woke up the neighborhood.
5. Mom's angry face told me I was in trouble.
6. The shoppers' brown bags were filled with groceries.
7. The bird's nest held three eggs.
8. Billy's puppies are learning tricks.
9. The fisherman's net held fish.
10. The car's engine made horrible clunking sounds.

Page 37

1. boxes
2. toys
3. children
4. men
5. lamps
6. puppies
7. geese
8. brushes
9. potatoes
10. cucumbers
11. clocks
12. mice
13. babies
14. wolves
15. crocodiles

Grammar, Usage, and Mechanics

A nonfiction reading & writing program • A nonfiction reading & writing program

Answer Key (cont.)

Page 38

Sentences may vary somewhat.

1. Plumbers fix pipes.
2. Apes swing from vines.
3. Bananas are delicious.
4. Seven boys and four girls are in my class.
5. The trains are coming down the track.
6. Pick one potato from our garden.
7. Teachers give us good books to read at home.
8. My feet hurt from walking ten miles barefoot.
9. One mouse just ran past me!
10. Will you set the table with these knives, forks, and spoons?

Page 39

1. haven't
2. They'll
3. couldn't
4. would've
5. Can't, I'm
6. I'll
7. won't
8. I've, she's, I'm
9. We're, can't
10. I'll, you've

Page 40

1. Martha could've been a dancer, but she preferred gymnastics.
2. I don't think I'll go to the nurse even though my throat hurts.
3. Rodriguez doesn't know the area well because he just moved here.
4. Our science teacher thinks we'll do well on the state test.
5. He's not only my brother, but he's also my best friend.
6. Don't be afraid of the dark because I'll leave a light on in the hallway.
7. The petshop owner told me the parrot would talk, but it won't even though I've done exactly what he said.
8. Let's go to the park tomorrow.
9. William can't make me go on the roller coaster.
10. I can't wait until tomorrow because we're going to the computer lab.

Page 43

1. I would like to know if I'll be able to compete in the gymnastics competition.
2. Nancy thought I could wear my blue leotard.
3. If I do well on the balance beam, I could get a medal.
4. I wonder what music I should use for my floor routine?
5. I do love gymnastics!
6. Uncle Bill is a Californian.
7. He is called Dr. Longley by his patients.
8. My uncle is a pediatrician.
9. When I see him, I always joke and say, "What's up, Doc?"
10. Uncle Bill is great to have around, because we always have a doctor in the house!

Grammar, Usage, and Mechanics

A nonfiction reading & writing program • A nonfiction reading & writing program

Answer Key (cont.)

Page 48

1. Mr. Ling, my music teacher, passed out our new song sheets.
2. You would like my dog, Charlie.
3. Soda, my favorite drink, was served at the party!
4. Could I have the book, *Freckle Face*, on your desk?
5. Yes, I would like some syrup for my pancakes, please.
6. When she told the policeman, Officer Pat, she felt relieved.
7. I told Billy, my next-door neighbor, that I accidentally broke his window.
8. A cardinal, my grandmother's favorite bird, bathed in the bird bath.
9. No, you can't play outside in the thunderstorm.
10. Mr. PJ's, a comic strip character, now has a computer game based on his adventures.

Page 52

1. "Good luck in your game!" Mom called.
2. "Thanks," I said, and laced up my cleats.
3. "Don't forget your knapsack," Mom warned.
4. "Why?" I asked.
5. "Well," Mom replied, "I put juice and cookies in it."
6. "Mom," I whispered as I hugged her, "you're the greatest."
7. "You, too, champ!" she said.
8. I asked, "Are you coming to my game?"
9. Mom laughed, "I wouldn't miss it for the world."
10. "Good," I answered, "now I know I'll play better."

Page 54

1. I/draw with a crayon.
2. The crayon/lay on the table.
3. We/sailed past the lighthouse.
4. The lighthouse/is one mile from shore.
5. The train/is coming shortly.
6. I/ride the train to work.
7. I/collected shells at the beach.
8. Shells/hid beneath the sand.
9. A napkin/is on my lap for emergencies.
10. My face/should be wiped with a napkin.

Page 55

Sentences may vary.

1. After the fire, we left our house and went to my aunt's house. She let us stay there until the firemen told us it was safe to return home.
2. When you do homework, first you should find a nice, quiet place to study. Make sure you have everything you need, like pencils and paper. You should turn off the television, too.
3. Babysitting is hard work, especially after a long day at school. When I have gym class and scooter races I get tired. Now, there are two kids who want to go to the playground!
4. I love reading. It is so great! You get caught up in the book. Sometimes, you actually think you are in the book!
5. When I go to sleepovers, I bring my sleeping bag. I also bring my favorite stuffed animal, but I hide it at the bottom of my sleeping bag. If other kids take out their stuffed animals, then I take mine out. If they don't, I keep it hidden so others don't think I'm a baby.

Grammar, Usage, and Mechanics

A nonfiction reading & writing program • *A nonfiction reading & writing program*

Answer Key (cont.)

Page 56

Sentences will vary.

Page 57

1. declarative
2. interrogative
3. exclamatory
4. imperative
5. exclamatory
6. imperative
7. interrogative
8. declarative
9. interrogative
10. imperative
11. exclamatory
12. declarative

Page 59

Sentences may vary slightly.

1. Joshua ate a hamburger and French fries.
2. Terrence hit the drum and the cymbals.
3. Grandpa read a book and the newspaper.
4. Chickens and roosters clucked in the farmyard.
5. Boys and girls played on the playground.
6. Mom bought peas, bread, and milk at the grocery store.
7. A bluebird, a cardinal, and a chickadee ate at the birdfeeder.
8. The campers roasted marshmallows and hot dogs over the campfire.

Page 60

All sentences will vary.

Page 61

1. I
2. I
3. me
4. me
5. I
6. I
7. I
8. me
9. I, I
10. I
11. I
12. me

Page 62

1. It's
2. It's
3. its
4. it's
5. its
6. Its
7. its
8. its
9. It's, its
10. its

Grammar, Usage, and Mechanics

A nonfiction reading & writing program • A nonfiction reading & writing program

Answer Key *(cont.)*

Page 64

1. Doesn't belong: umbrella

   things you can play with in the sand or ground

2. Doesn't belong: lipstick

   things you put in your hair

3. Doesn't belong: shoes

   things you need at bedtime

4. Doesn't belong: apple

   desk supplies

Page 65

All paragraphs will vary.

Page 66

Sentences that do not belong:

   It is high tide.

   Fish eat smaller fish.

   I wonder if my mom misses me?

   Type of Paragraph: Narrative/Descriptive

Sentences that do not belong:

   Riding the school bus is fun.

   I have a map of the United States.

   Cars go when there is a green light.

   Type of Paragraph: How-to

Page 67

Sentences will vary.

Page 69

1. Maybe we should buy our apples over there.

2. I don't know why she always talks with her mouth full.

3. Tomorrow we're going to wear our beautiful dresses to school.

4. Two elephants wandered by us, and we threw peanuts to them.

5. In soccer, you need to kick the ball with your feet and not use your hands.

Corrected paragraph:

   There is a large oak tree in my backyard. I have always wanted to make a big pile of leaves to jump in. My dad spends so much time raking, he always says, "No leaf pile. I've done enough raking this year." Then my dad got a leaf blower. We were excited to see if it worked. My mom handed us rakes and we hoped we wouldn't be left raking the millions of oak leaves. My dad filled the engine of the leaf blower with gasoline and pulled the handle. The leaf blower made a loud noise, but it did a great job. We had so much fun rolling in the leaves and throwing them into the air. My mom said to my dad, "Honey, do you think we should get a snow blower, too?"

Answer Key *(cont.)*

Page 70

Adjectives in the sentences will vary.

1. For Halloween, I love to wear costumes.

2. Isn't it a lovely day?

3. I love to eat ice cream!

4. Long-fin tuna swam in the Atlantic Ocean in August.

5. A huge bird flew over my house.

6. Did you hear the loud siren?

7. "Hey, Mr. Spenser!" I called. "Can you help mom and me fix my bike?"

8. "This is my favorite song," said Lisa.

9. Aren't we supposed to buy ice cream, hot fudge, whipped cream, and cherries for the party we're having tonight?

10. We'll call you before the show. You'll be home, won't you?